Davi KU-747-092

Moles

Anthony Nelson

© 1986 The Mammal Society
First published in 1986 by Anthony Nelson Ltd
PO Box 9, Oswestry, Shropshire SY11 1BY, England.

All rights reserved. No part of this book may be reproduced, stored
in a retrieval system, or transmitted in any form or by any means,
electronic, mechanical, photocopying or otherwise, without the
permission of the publisher.

Series editor Robert Burton
Diagrams by Robert Donaldson
Drawings by Graham Allen: 17, 18
Photographs by Jane Burton: cover, 3, 5, 12 (bottom), inside back
cover; Martin Gorman: inside front cover (top); Andy Lucas: 4; Pat
Morris: 1, 7, 12 (top), 14 (top); David Stone: inside front cover
(bottom)

Royalties from this series will go to the Mammal Society

ISBN 0 904614 16 6

Designed by Alan Bartram
Printed by Livesey Ltd, 7 St John's Hill, Shrewsbury

Inside front cover
Top: A mole emerges from the ground.
Bottom: The forelimb is built like an excavator bucket.

The European mole is one of the most common small mammals in Britain and its voracious appetite has earned it the title of subterranean 'predator-in-chief'. Despite its widespread distribution, few people have seen a live mole. This is because moles spend most of their lives within a system of tunnels beneath the soil, and their presence is conveyed by the molehills on the surface. Being relatively safe underground, these shy, secretive animals rarely venture to the surface, where they are easy prey for many hunting animals.

By virtue of its anatomical and sensory specialisations, the mole has proved highly successful in exploiting its underground environment. As moles are such difficult animals to observe, it is not surprising that little is known about their behaviour and ecology. By following moles fitted with miniature radio transmitters, I have been able to study their behaviour and life-style.

The common, or European, mole *Talpa europaea* is an insectivore, of the family Talpidae whose members are widespread through most of Europe, Asia and North America. The family includes other burrowing species such as Brewer's mole, the semi-aquatic star-nosed moles and desmans, and others, such as shrew moles, which are largely terrestrial.

Description

The mole is highly specialised for a subterranean, digging way of life. The broad, spade-like forelimbs, which have developed as powerful digging

Skeleton of a mole showing the strength of the forelimb and its extra bone.

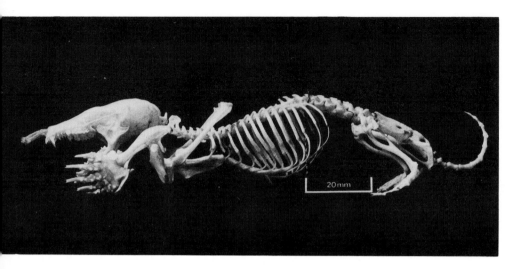

organs, are attached to muscular shoulders and a deep chestbone. The skin of
the chest is thicker than elsewhere on the body, as this region supports the
most weight when the mole digs or sleeps. Behind the enormous shoulders,
the body is almost cylindrical, tapering slightly to narrow hips, short sturdy
limbs, which are not especially adapted for digging, and a short club-shaped
tail, which is usually carried erect. Both pairs of limbs bear an extra bone,
which increases the surface area of the paws, for support in the hindlimbs
and for moving earth in the forelimbs.

The elongated head tapers to a hairless, fleshy, pink snout which is highly
sensory. The entire body, with the exception of the feet, snout and mouth is
covered in soft thick silver-black fur, which hides the small eyes and ears.

Measurements

The length of the body from head to tail ranges from 140–170 millimetres in
males and 120–150 millimetres in females. Body weights vary considerably
according to the time of year and the weight of stomach contents when the
animal is weighed. In general, males are heavier than females, although as
there is such a considerable amount of overlap between the sexes in both
length and weight, these criteria are not reliable for sexing individuals.
Towards the end of the year, during October and November, males weigh
around 95 grams (range 80–105 grams), and females at this stage weigh 75
grams (range 60—85 grams). Lower weights of both sexes indicate the
presence of juveniles in the population. Peak weights are reached in April for
males, which may weigh over 120 grams, whereas females, prior to giving
birth in June, attain maximum weights of over 105 grams.

4

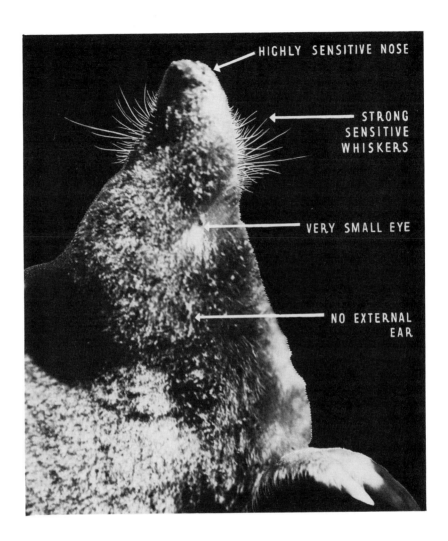

HIGHLY SENSITIVE NOSE

STRONG SENSITIVE WHISKERS

VERY SMALL EYE

NO EXTERNAL EAR

Senses

Our knowledge of the sensory world of the mole is very limited. The main senses are thought to be touch and smell. The pink, fleshy snout, which is richly supplied in blood vessels and nerve endings, also bears sensory organs, known as Eimer's organs. These detect changes in humidity and temperature as well as being sensitive to touch. The backs of the forefeet bear a stiff fringe of hairs, which are also believed to have a sensory function.

The apparent absence of ears is due to the lack of external flaps, the thick fur and also the unusual position of the ear openings, which are level with the corner of the mouth. They are more obvious in young animals than in adults, because of the thinner hair. A circular opening, 2 millimetres in diameter and bordered by short fine hairs, leads to the inner ear structures. Although a mole's hearing is not very sharp, it does detect and respond to sudden noises. Captive moles quickly associate certain sounds with feeding times, such as knocking on their nest box, or even calling their name! Moles utter both very low twittering sounds and very high pitched shrieks, and it is possible that they emit and perceive sounds which are outside the scope of human hearing, perhaps like the ultrasonic calls of bats.

The mole's sense of vision is quite poor when compared with other small mammals. It is not, however, completely blind as is commonly believed. In adults, the eyes measure only 1 millimetre in diameter and, although all of the functional parts of an eye which ensure normal vision are present, certain features are poorly developed. It is likely that, whereas the mole almost certainly cannot focus rapidly on distant objects, it is able to perceive certain features such as a source of light, its intensity and sudden movements near to it.

The sense of smell appears to be important in finding food at short range only, although moles are able to detect water from much greater distances. When a mole is active in its tunnels, the moist snout is continually moving and is usually kept very close to the ground. In an open space the nose is raised and the mole occasionally lifts itself onto its rear limbs in an effort to sample the air more successfully. Moles possess many scent glands, the secretions of which are detected by their sense of smell. It is believed that some of these secretions are used in marking their individual territories and thus function as a means of communicating with neighbouring animals.

In addition to these senses, it is believed that the mole has a well developed kinaesthetic sense, or sense of orientation. This is thought to aid in forming and retaining a mental plan of its underground environment, such as the complex layout of its tunnels, so that it can easily find its way around. It must, for instance, be keenly aware of the spatial arrangement of its tunnels if they are to be linked together.

The coat

The fur of the 'little gentleman in black velvet' is composed of two types of hair: a thick pile of short hairs, interspersed with larger, coarse, guard hairs. The uniform texture of the fur allows it to lie in any direction, which makes it easier to reverse rapidly among the tunnels, as when retreating from danger.

A complete change of coat, except for the fringe hairs on the feet and tail, occurs in all individuals during the spring and autumn. In some areas of Britain a brief summer moult may occur, although this may be the result of an extended spring moult. The moult lasts for three to four weeks with great variation in the moulting times of different individuals, even within the same locality. The spring moult always begins on the underside of the body,

Tracks show the mole's belly dragging in the mud and the unusual prints left by the forelimbs.

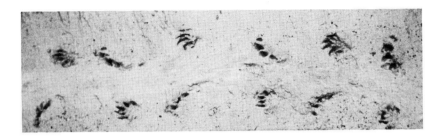

spreading from the breast patch around the forelegs to the shoulders, and then posteriorally along the sides and back to the rump. During the autumn moult, which replaces the summer pelage with longer fur, the moult pattern is reversed. Beginning at the rump, the moult extends towards the head, while at the same time progressing towards the flanks. The underside is usually the last part of the body to moult at this time.

Colour variants

Many colour variations have been reported in the past by mole trappers. These include slate-grey, cinnamon brown, piebald (dark with light patches on the underside) and smoky (yellow-grey). There are also some records of albino moles. Yellow-tinted hairs are common on the underside of the body and, although earlier writers believed this to be some type of colour variation, it is now thought to be the result of staining by specialised skin glands

Distribution

The European mole is widespread in western Europe and may be found throughout the British mainland and on the offshore islands of Skye, Mull, Wight, Alderney, Anglesey and Jersey. It is not, however, present in Ireland. Moles may be found wherever the soil is deep enough to form a system of tunnels, and is sufficiently enriched with humus to support a population of soil invertebrates.

Although moles were originally inhabitants of deciduous woodlands they have taken advantage of current trends in agriculture, and readily colonise fertile pasture and arable fields. Other habitats where moles occur include young coniferous forests, moorlands, roadside verges and stable sand dunes. Moles have been recorded at altitudes of up to 1,000 metres.

Population characteristics

Within a natural population the sexes are equally represented for most of the year. However, during the breeding season, the number of males present is often double that of females, as they actively search for females in reproductive condition. This increase in the male sex ratio is due to an influx of neighbouring or transient males into the population and also an increase in the mobility and searching rate of the males within the existing population.

The density of moles within a region varies considerably according to the quality of the habitat, the availability and abundance of prey items being the most important factors in determining the density. Deciduous woodlands and permanent pastures, both highly fertile areas, support a mean density of four and five moles per hectare respectively. By comparison, in areas which do not support high densities of prey items, such as young coniferous plantations or moorland, the density of moles may be as low as one per hectare.

The average lifespan of a mole is 2½ years, although the majority never reach maturity (1 year old), and only very few live to be five years old. Within a population, juveniles are the most abundant group (45 per cent), followed by one- or two-year olds (40 per cent) and two- to three-year olds (13 per cent). The remaining two per cent are over three years old.

Burrowing

The function of a mole's burrow has been misinterpreted by many people. Moles do not dig constantly or specifically in search of food. Instead, the tunnel system, which is the permanent habitation of the mole, acts as a food trap, constantly collecting invertebrate prey such as earthworms and insect larvae. As they move through the soil, invertebrates fall into the mole run and often do not escape before being detected by the patrolling resident.

Tunnel construction and maintenance occupy much of a mole's active time. Moles dig actively throughout the year although once it has established its burrow system, there may be little evidence above ground of its presence. The exceptions to this are the onset of the breeding season, when males greatly extend their tunnels, and during periods of cold weather.

As a result of a fall in soil temperature, earthworms and soil insects are either immobilised near the surface, or they dig deeper into the earth where soil temperatures are higher. At such times moles will not collect enough food in their surface tunnels to survive, so they too must retreat deeper into the soil and construct additional tunnels. Thus fresh mole-hills are commonly seen during periods of frost and snow.

Molehills are not permanent features and are gradually broken down by trampling animals and rainfall. On one occasion I captured over 20 moles within a pasture field, although there were only four molehills to be seen. Thus one cannot estimate a mole population simply by counting the number of molehills.

Early naturalists assumed that the mole lifted loose earth with its head.

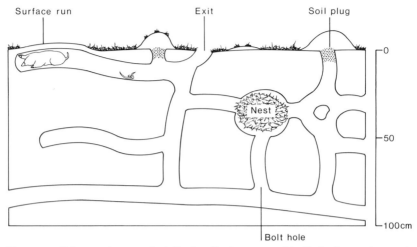

However, it is now known that the forelimbs are used both for loosening and moving the soil. The bone structure and muscular arrangement of a mole are unique and are designed primarily for digging and scooping loose soil along their flanks, as well as for propelling the mole through its tunnels.

The deep, keel-shaped breastbone is the site of attachment for the major muscles involved in digging and locomotion. When the muscles connecting the bone with the shoulderblade contract and relax, the humerus (the short, thickened armbone between the shoulders and elbow) moves back and forth. As the humerus rotates, the forearm and digits which are set at an angle (as if the arm is permanently crooked), move through an arc. Additional muscles move the individual digits. All the movements of the forelimbs, whether digging or moving, depend on the same sequence of muscular actions. When on a level surface, outside its tunnel, moles 'walk' in a rather ungainly fashion with only the base of the paws of the forelimbs touching the surface. When a mole is reversing down its tunnel, the body and forelimbs are pulled along by the hindlimbs.

There are three main types of tunnel. Temporary surface runs in the form of shallow trenches may be created in soft, freshly cultivated earth, or in sandy soils, using both forelimbs simultaneously in a 'breast-stroke', swimming action. This action may also be observed when a mole is frightened and attempts to rapidly bury itself. Such runs are often used only once, and are usually for purely exploratory purposes. They are most common in the breeding season and were aptly termed 'traces d'amour', or 'courtship runs' by early French naturalists.

Shallow tunnels (8–10 centimetres below the surface) can be seen in the form of a raised ridge in the soil and they do not require the physical removal of the earth from the tunnels, nor the formation of molehills. To dig a shallow tunnel, the mole braces one of its forelimbs beneath its body on the floor of

9

the run, while it digs and pushes the soil upward with the other. The upward thrust of the forelimbs presses the body against the opposite wall of the run, thereby compacting the soil of the tunnel wall. After three or four strokes with one paw, the mole rotates its body through 180° and digs with the other. This alternation serves to rest the muscles of each limb, while at the same time ensuring the correct width of the tunnel.

When deeper, permanent tunnels are being dug, a mole initially loosens the soil with its forelimbs and then pushes it back along its flank with each thrust of its paws. The loose earth is then kicked back along the tunnel by the hindlimbs. After a quantity of loose earth has accumulated behind the mole, it stops digging and turns completely around by somersaulting, to face the loose earth. This is collected and pushed, using alternate paws, along the tunnel, to a previously dug vertical or sloping shaft leading to the surface. The earth is again pushed up this shaft with alternate paws, by bracing the body against the side of the tunnel and pushing the soil upwards. This loose earth makes up the characteristic volcano-shaped spoil heaps or molehills. Moles commonly make use of old shafts during periods of drought, or when the earth's surface is frozen, as the soil within the shaft is not encrusted or solid. New vertical shafts to facilitate the removal of loose earth are dug when the tunnel system is being enlarged.

The tunnel system

Moles construct a complex system of burrows. In shallow soil the burrows may be largely on one level, but they usually form a multi-tiered pattern. When a mole begins to excavate a tunnel system it makes an initial, relatively straight, exploratory tunnel for up to 15 metres, before adding side branches. This is, presumably, an attempt to locate neighbouring animals, while at the same time forming a food trap for later use. These tunnels will later be lengthened, and many more will be formed beneath these preliminary burrows. This tiered effect of tunnels can result in the burrows of one animal actually overlying those of its neighbours without being joined together. However, in an established population, many tunnels between neighbouring animals are directly connected.

Moles possess a keen sense of orientation, and may often reconstruct their tunnels in exactly the same place each year. In permanent pastures, existing tunnels may be used by many generations of moles. Some animals may be evicted from their own tunnels by the invasion of a stronger neighbouring mole and on such occasions will have to disperse and establish a new tunnel system. Moles regularly change the shape of their territory, although, with the exception of the breeding season, the actual area occupied does not vary to a great extent. Although individual moles are continually changing the design of their burrows, they usually retain the same nest site, which is usually located near the centre of the territory.

Moles are highly familiar with each part of their own territory and are suspicious of any changes in a tunnel. If the route to the nest or feeding area is blocked off, they usually dig around or under the obstacle, such as a mole trap, to rejoin the original tunnel with a minimum amount of digging.

The nest

The mole generally occupies one main nest, although short periods of rest may be taken in the tunnel. During the breeding season, females may occupy two or more nests, and the juveniles may be moved to another nest if the original is disturbed. Nesting material is usually gathered from the surface; and the mole emerges briefly from its tunnel to gather material from the immediate vicinity of the hole. It will, occasionally, venture completely into the open to obtain dry material, but rarely strays far from the tunnel entrance. Nesting material is carried in the mouth.

An enlarged part of a deep tunnel serves as the nest chamber, which is usually partially filled with dry grasses or leaves, although newspapers and potato crisp packets have also been used! The material is usually woven into a spherical ball, and the entrance to the nest is not very obvious. When in the nest, the mole pulls the bedding material closely around itself before it sleeps. On the surface there are no visible signs of this type of nest, as it may be formed at varying depths anywhere within the tunnel system.

When the soil is shallow, or in lowlying areas subject to flooding, larger molehills, often incorporating nest chambers and bedding material, may be formed. These large constructions are known as 'fortresses', and may be formed by either male and female, but are not, as was commonly believed, built only during the breeding season. Fortresses differ from the structureless molehills in that they are usually much larger (up to 1 metre high), often containing a nest chamber and several radial tunnels. The specific function of a mole's fortress is not yet fully understood.

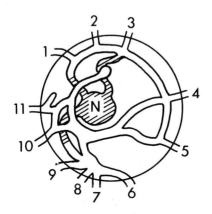

Top: A 'fortress' excavated to show the nest above the water table.
Bottom: Underground mole nests are sometimes exposed during excavation work.

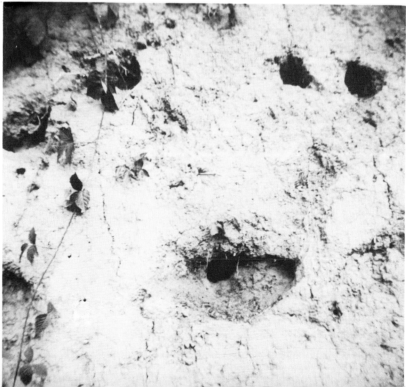

Breeding

The breeding season spans late February to early June, often beginning one month later in Scotland than in the south of England. This may be due to environmental factors such as soil temperature. During much of the year, the sex glands and reproductive tracts of both sexes are very small and show no signs of activity, but as the breeding season approaches they undergo rapid development. These glands regress when the season is finished.

The period of time during which females are in oestrous and receptive to the male is usually very short, probably only three or four days. This is the only time of the year when female moles will tolerate the presence of males within their territory. Males probably determine the reproductive status of a female by smell. There are few accounts of the mating behaviour of moles and it is not known if females mate with only one or with several males. The adult males do not help in rearing the young.

Following a gestation period of four weeks, the young are born in the nest, during April or May in southern England and June or July in Scotland. The female mole has four pairs of nipples suggesting that eight young could be suckled, although the average litter size is only four. Newborn moles are pink and hairless, and they already show the massive development of the shoulders and front limbs. Weighing only 3.5 grams at birth, they are unable to move around, and their mother makes many brief journeys to collect food so that she is never absent from the nest for too long.

Newborn moles cannot control their body temperature very successfully and rely on their mother for warmth. After about two weeks their fur begins to grow, and they appear a dark brownish-black.

The young moles are fed entirely on milk for the first month, and rapidly gain weight. At the end of three weeks, most weigh about 60 grams and are almost 120 millimetres long. The tail and hind feet are fully developed and the sexes can be distinguished at this stage. The eyes usually open by the fourth week, and the body is covered in a beautiful coat of shimmering silver-black fur.

Juvenile moles remain in the nest until they are about five weeks old, when they begin to make short, exploratory forays in the immediate vicinity of the nest chamber. On such trips they are usually accompanied by their mother. Two weeks later they are actively exploring and searching for their food, within the tunnel system. They continue to share the parent's range for another two weeks, before dispersing in search of their own home range. It is possible that at this stage the mother becomes more aggressive towards the young, forcing them to leave her tunnel system.

At nine weeks, now fully developed and only slightly smaller than adult females, juvenile moles attempt to establish their own tunnel system. When they leave the maternal burrows, they usually come to the surface and wander around, occasionally digging into the soil in an attempt to start a tunnel. They appear to be rather inadequate at digging initially, although

Top: A baby mole, about one week old.
Bottom: The breeding cycle of moles in Scotland.

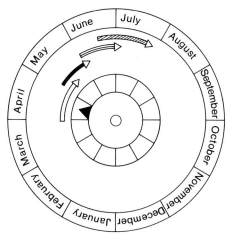

➱ Juvenile dispersion
➱ Lactation
➡ Gestation
➱ Mating
(○) Peak weights for gonad, body and scent glands.

they soon become quite adept. It is during this period that moles are most likely to be seen on the surface. Many juveniles stray into the tunnel systems of neighbouring resident moles and search for food until discovered, whereupon they are speedily evicted.

The juvenile dispersal phase is the critical period in the life of a mole because of its vulnerability on the surface. By remaining concealed under leaves or grass many juveniles avoid predators; others fail to establish their own tunnel systems and die from starvation.

Young moles that succeed in creating their own burrows will commence breeding during the following year. Moles in Britain usually breed once a year, although second litters have occasionally been discovered in southern England and they are common in Europe.

Feeding habits

Before the middle of the nineteenth century, the mole was considered to be omnivorous, devouring not only earthworms and insect larvae, but also turnips, carrots and other root crops. This confusion is probably due to the fact that, on the Continent, several species of voles, which feed only on roots, may occupy the same tunnels as moles. The truth is that moles are true carnivores, feeding almost exclusively on earthworms and the larvae of beetles and flies.

An adult mole requires up to 50 grams of food, or half its body weight, each day to survive. Moles are, to a certain extent, opportunistic predators and will sample almost any type of insect larva they may discover in their tunnels. They have also been known to scavenge on dead mice, birds and frogs and it has been suggested that moles frequently revert to cannibalism. This is, however, rather unlikely to occur, apart from adult females killing their young if continually disturbed at the nest site, or under extreme environmental conditions leading to a shortage of food.

A mole may obtain its food in three ways.
1. while constructing its tunnels,
2. by travelling along the tunnel system, and
3. searching the surface, where it may catch earthworms (particularly during a rain shower following a very dry spell) or scavenge on dead animals.

Of these three techniques, the second is usually the most profitable.

Moles are believed to locate their prey by smell. The range of perception is limited to about 10 centimetres, and moles often stumble across their prey before actually detecting it. Once aware of the presence of food, the head is moved from side to side, with the snout continually twitching. If the prey is not located, the mole will move to and fro in the tunnel, or if space permits, circle around, until it is found.

Food is always seized between the front paws, with the body lowered to the ground and the hind limbs set far apart for support. The digits of the

The diet of moles changes in the summer when there are more insect larvae.

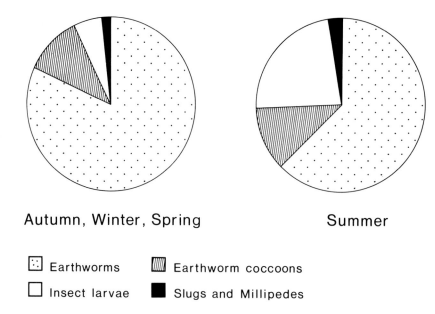

Autumn, Winter, Spring   Summer

:: Earthworms   ▥ Earthworm coccoons
☐ Insect larvae   ■ Slugs and Millipedes

front feet cannot be flexed to seize prey so it has to be trapped between both front paws and raised to the mouth. Small earthworms and soft-bodied larvae are eaten whole, by starting at one end and pulling the body between the forefeet with upward jerks of the head. When a worm is eaten in this manner, much of the gut contents are forced out of the body and remain on the paws. Larger earthworms are seized in the front paws and rapidly decapitated. If the worm is caught in the middle or by the tail, it is usually twisted around until the head is between the front paws.

Large earthworms are often stored, especially towards the end of the spring and autumn, perhaps in anticipation of adverse climatic conditions, such as dry or very cold periods, when soil invertebrates retreat deeper into the soil. At such times, when earthworms are scarce, moles eat more insect larvae than at any other time of year. If presented with a surplus of earthworms, moles will take many of them to one or more stores, often near the nest. The heads of the earthworms are usually removed to prevent escape. It is not known if moles return to recover all of their stores during periods of food storage.

Despite the fact that much of the mole's prey is composed of fluids, it still requires a great deal of water to drink. During a period of drought, moles may travel over 2 kilometres to reach a permanent source of water. Moles have also been observed coming to the surface early in the morning and drinking dew off the grass. Whether this is their sole purpose in coming to the surface is not known.

16

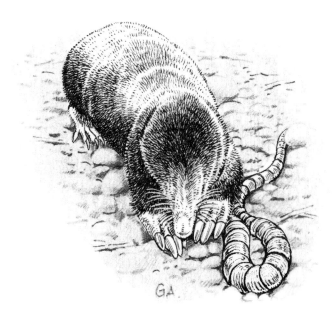

Social behaviour

Moles are largely solitary and, with the exception of a brief respite during the breeding season, they are highly aggressive towards other moles, of either sex. Each mole maintains its own set of tunnels, which it has either constructed itself, or occupied following the emigration, death or eviction of the former owner. The resources within the tunnels must be sufficient to support the daily requirements of the resident mole. This defended area is known as its territory.

The size of the territory depends on the sex of the individual, the habitat and the season. The territory of an adult male is always larger than that of a female, and ranges from 3,000 square metres during the summer to 7,000 square metres during the breeding season. In contrast, female territories remain relatively constant at 2,000 square metres throughout the year. Poorer quality habitats, such as moorland or sand dunes, where prey density is low, result in larger territories when compared with woodlands and arable land, where prey density is higher.

Each mole visits most of its territory on a daily basis, thereby familiarising itself with its own tunnel system. The tunnels of neighbouring moles are often connected, and although animals rarely meet, they are aware of a neighbour's presence. Neighbouring moles avoid direct confrontation by each foraging in the areas of overlap during different periods of activity.

Following the death, or artificial removal of a mole from its territory, neighbouring animals will invade and often usurp this vacant space within

Territorial systems: (left) a stable pattern of four moles, with the male's territory overlapping those of three females; (right) when one female disappeared, her neighbours soon noticed her absence and quickly occupied the vacant space.

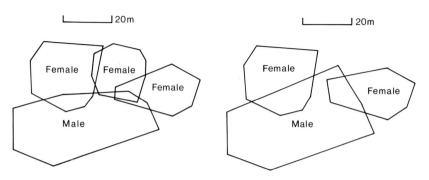

Moles fighting. One is defending itself by using a forelimb as a shield.

24 hours. Whereas the central space of a mole's territory is rarely violated by neighbouring animals (as long as the resident is present), peripheral zones are heavily used and shared by neighbouring moles. Thus, depending on the population density, the shape and size of a mole's territory may alter quite frequently.

One mystery, still unsolved, is the use of communal tunnels, which may be shared by many individuals. On many occasions 10–12 moles have been captured, using a single trap in the same position, over a period of 24 hours. Such communal runs are usually access routes to a vital resource, such as a

Daily activity cycle of an individual mole.

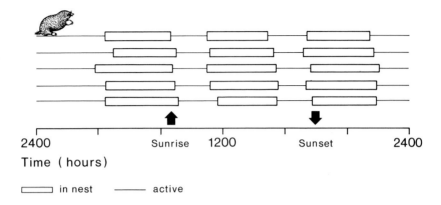

Time (hours)

⎯⎯⎯ in nest   ——— active

stream. When two moles do meet, a short fight may occur, with both animals trying to bite and scratch their opponent. A brief chase usually ensues, resulting in the eviction of the intruder.

Activity

Moles are active during the day and night, throughout the year. They do not hibernate or aestivate, as was once believed. Periods of activity last from 4 to 4½ hours, and are interrupted for brief periods of rest, which are usually taken at irregular intervals in the tunnels. In between there are periods of inactivity lasting 3½ to 4 hours, spent at the main nest. This pattern is usually repeated three times over a 24-hour period.

When active, moles forage in their burrows for prey, enlarge or repair damaged tunnels, or groom. This accounts for over 55 per cent of each day. Of this fraction, 49 per cent is spent moving, 41 per cent digging and approximately 10 per cent dozing in the tunnels, away from the main nest. These values change between individuals and seasons. During the breeding season males often leave their own territories in search of females for short periods. They may not return to the main nest for several days, during which time they sleep briefly in the tunnels. Another variation in the basic activity rhythm is noticed when females have given birth. During the lactation period, females make many brief forays in search of food, so that the regular pattern of activity is disrupted by numerous shorter feeding bouts and rests at the nest.

Predators and mortality

Man must certainly be the greatest predator of moles. This persecution results from the damage caused to crops, lawns and golf courses by molehills. In addition, until 1950, there was a strong market in the sale of moleskins.

Fortunately, for the moles at least, fashions changed to more readily available woollen and synthetic materials. At the peak of this trade, America was importing over four million moleskins a year from England. Moleskin coats, trousers and waistcoats were once highly prized, especially since it took over 100 good pelts to make both front pieces of a waistcoat!

Natural predation on juveniles is heavy, during the dispersal phase, from such predators as tawny owls, herons, buzzards, foxes and small carnivores. Domestic cats frequently kill moles, although they rarely eat them. The mortality rates for both juveniles and adults also increase during periods of drought, when prey become scarce.

The mole is a host for many species of parasites, especially fleas, many of which are host specific. Mites have also been recovered frequently from live moles and the nesting material. Moles also carry several internal parasites although, as the degree of infestation is usually quite low, they rarely result in the mole's death.

Tooth wear in moles is quite severe, due to ingestion of so much grit with their prey, but the damage is rarely such that chewing becomes impossible, and mortality arising directly from this cause is rare.

Relations with Man

The mole is considered a pest by gardeners, greenkeepers and farmers alike. Its burrowing habits result in raised tunnels and molehills which bring stones to the surface, thereby damaging agricultural machinery and reducing the crop yield. Exposed soil heaps are rapidly colonised by weeds, which may subsequently spread through the crop. Soil from molehills collected with a silage crop results in fouling and waste in the yield. In recently tilled fields, mole runs made along the drills of root and grain crops may disturb their roots to such an extent that the plants wilt and die.

Most of the damage caused by moles occurs before and during the breeding season, when the tunnel systems are being enlarged. Damage is also significant in recently sown fields, as the mole is forced to rebuild its tunnel system following its destruction by farm machinery. On the positive side, moles may be beneficial to farmers and gardeners by preying on insect larvae, such as cockchafers and wireworms, which can cause considerable damage to crops, In addition, the moles' tunnels help to aerate the soil while, to a lesser extent, they also act as drainage channels. However this is of limited use because moles rarely tunnel in water-logged soils.